Contents

An Interview with Nixie Labs

Nixie Labs, Inc. is an American company based in Silicon Valley in California. The team of scientists and engineers at Nixie Labs is developing the world's first small, wearable camera drone. In this interview, a computer scientist from Nixie Labs explains the project.

Floris Ernst is a computer scientist working on the Nixie drone's flight control systems. We asked him about the project and his work...

What are you making?
'I'm helping to create Nixie, a wearable camera drone. Nixie will be portable, automatic and help take spectacular pictures outdoors by automatically framing the user. I am working on the motion sensors and algorithms to make Nixie fly smoothly and accurately.'

5 **How did the Nixie project start?**
'Christoph, the inventor of Nixie, was inspired by the idea of a drone to help take photos of exciting outdoor sports like rock climbing. It's really hard to handle a camera while hanging on to a cliff, but there's potential for great pictures. Nixie could open up the sky to amateur photographers.'

10 **What makes this drone different?**
'Nixie is wearable! That makes it easy to transport and use anywhere. Most camera drones are bulky and slow to set up, and require a dedicated pilot or GPS-mapped flight plan. Nixie does one thing: take pictures of its owner. By automating this, we can refine the design so anyone can use it confidently.'

15 **Is it safe for people to use drones?**
'We're thinking a lot about safety. Automating its flight reduces pilot error. Nixie is small and light so it won't do major damage even if it crashes. But people will still need to think carefully and be considerate to others before they launch a Nixie. I personally don't like the idea of drones flying around and peeking into every hole.'

20 **How will Nixie be used?**
'We think Nixie will suit outdoor sportspeople, like rock climbers. But we've spoken to people in firefighting, where a cheap, quick drone to help them see a new high angle of a dangerous situation could help them a lot. Wearing a Nixie might also help locate people in alpine rescue or other emergency situations.'

25 **What's next for the Nixie project?**
'There's a lot of work to do! We need to work out the best shape to make Nixie a user-friendly wearable device. We're experimenting with how to control Nixie, such as with smartphones or gestures. And we need to improve how accurately Nixie can return to its owner once it's taken its pictures. It will be a busy year.'

From *http://antenna.sciencemuseum.org.uk*

1 **According to Floris Ernst, what "one thing" is Nixie designed to do?**

....

1 mark

2 **Why does Floris Ernst think Nixie will appeal to rock climbers?**

....

....

1 mark

3 **Why might camera drones like Nixie create concerns about people's privacy?**

....

....

....

2 marks

4 **Give two ways in which the emergency services could use camera drones.**

....

....

....

2 marks

5 **How do you think Floris Ernst feels about working on Nixie? Explain your answer.**

....

....

2 marks

6 **Do you think Nixie is a good invention? Explain your answer.**

....

....

....

2 marks

Total out of 10

Holes

Louis Sachar is an American author who has written many books for children. *Holes* is one of his most popular novels. It tells the story of Stanley, a boy cursed with bad luck. Due to a series of unfortunate events, Stanley finds himself at Camp Green Lake Juvenile Detention Centre...

There is no lake at Camp Green Lake. There once was a very large lake here, the largest lake in Texas. That was over a hundred years ago. Now it is just a dry, flat wasteland.

There used to be a town of Green Lake as well. The town shriveled and dried up along with the lake, and the people who lived there. (5)

During the summer the daytime temperature hovers around ninety-five degrees in the shade—if you can find any shade. There's not much shade in a big dry lake.

The only trees are two old oaks on the eastern edge of the "lake." A hammock is stretched between the two trees, and a log cabin stands behind that.

(10) The campers are forbidden to lie in the hammock. It belongs to the Warden. The Warden owns the shade.

Out on the lake, rattlesnakes and scorpions find shade under rocks and in the holes dug by the campers.

Here's a good rule to remember about rattlesnakes and scorpions: If you don't bother them, they won't bother you. (15)

Usually.

Being bitten by a scorpion or even a rattlesnake is not the worst thing that can happen to you. You won't die.

Usually.

(20) Sometimes a camper will try to be bitten by a scorpion, or even a small rattlesnake. Then he will get to spend a day or two recovering in his tent, instead of having to dig a hole out on the lake.

But you don't want to be bitten by a yellow-spotted lizard. That's the worst thing that can happen to you. You will die a slow and painful death. (25)

Always.

If you get bitten by a yellow-spotted lizard, you might as well go into the shade of the oak trees and lie in the hammock.

(30) There is nothing anyone can do to you anymore.

An extract from *Holes* by Louis Sachar.

1 Over a century ago, Camp Green Lake was very different to the way it is now. In what ways has the area changed over time?

....

....

1 mark

2 What is the narrator's attitude towards Camp Green Lake's location? Explain your answer.

....

....

....

2 marks

3 What type of person do you think the Warden is? Explain your answer.

....

....

2 marks

4 Do you think campers enjoy the activities at Camp Green Lake? Explain your answer.

....

....

....

2 marks

5 Identify one technique that Louis Sachar uses to make the reader want to read more.

....

....

1 mark

6 The boys at Camp Green Lake have been sent there as a punishment for bad behaviour. Do you think digging holes on the lake is a suitable punishment? Explain your answer.

....

....

....

2 marks

Total out of 10

Born on a Blue Day

This extract is from a book by Daniel Tammet called *Born on a Blue Day*. Daniel has savant syndrome and a form of Asperger's syndrome. This means he is incredibly intelligent and has an amazing memory, but he often has trouble interacting and communicating with others.

I was born on 31 January 1979 – a Wednesday. I know it was a Wednesday, because the date is blue in my mind and Wednesdays are always blue, like the number nine or the sound of loud voices arguing. I like my birth date, because of the way I'm able to visualise most of the numbers in it as smooth and round shapes, similar to 5 pebbles on a beach. That's because they are prime numbers: 31, 19, 197, 97, 79 and 1979 are all divisible only by themselves and one. I can recognise every prime up to 9973 by their 'pebble-like' quality. It's just the way my brain works.

I have a rare condition known as savant syndrome, little known before its portrayal by actor Dustin Hoffman in the Oscar-winning 1988 film *Rain Man*. Like 10 Hoffman's character, Raymond Babbitt, I have an almost obsessive need for order and routine, which affects virtually every aspect of my life. For example, I eat exactly 45 grams of porridge for breakfast each morning; I weigh the bowl with an electronic scale to make sure. Then I count the number of items of clothing I'm wearing before I leave my house. I get anxious if I can't drink my cups of tea at the same time each 15 day. Whenever I become too stressed and I can't breathe properly, I close my eyes and count. Thinking of numbers helps me to become calm again.

Numbers are my friends and they are always around me. Each one is unique and has its own personality. Eleven is friendly and five is loud, whereas four is both shy and quiet – it's my favourite number, perhaps because it reminds me of myself. Some 20 are big – 23, 667, 1179 – while others are small: 6, 13, 581. Some are beautiful, like 333, and some are ugly, like 289. To me, every number is special.

No matter where I go or what I'm doing, numbers are never far from my thoughts. In an interview with chat show host David Letterman in New York, I told David he looked like the number 117 – tall and lanky. Later outside, in the 25 appropriately numerically named Times Square, I gazed up at the towering skyscrapers and felt surrounded by nines – the number I most associate with feelings of immensity.

Scientists call my visual, emotional experience of numbers synaesthesia, a rare neurological mixing of the senses, which most commonly results in the ability to see alphabetical letters and/or numbers in colour. Mine is an unusual and complex type, 30 through which I see numbers as shapes, colours, textures and motions. The number one, for example, is a brilliant and bright white, like someone shining a torch beam into my eyes. Five is a clap of thunder or the sound of waves crashing against rocks. Thirty-seven is lumpy like porridge, while eighty-nine reminds me of falling snow.

An extract from *Born on a Blue Day* by Daniel Tammet.

1. **What is a prime number? How is Daniel able to recognise them?**

....

....

2 marks

2. **Describe Daniel's morning routine. What happens if he doesn't follow his regular routine?**

....

....

....

2 marks

3. **Find two examples of personification in this passage.**

....

....

1 mark

4. **Why does Daniel describe Times Square as being "numerically named" (line 25)?**

....

1 mark

5. **What does Daniel mean when he says he "felt surrounded by nines" (line 26)?**

....

....

2 marks

6. **What do you think it would be like to live with savant syndrome?**

....

....

....

2 marks

Total out of 10

Hostages to Handheld Devices

Mobile phones, tablets and computers are now so popular that some children spend more time playing games on them than they do playing sports. Many people are worried that this is bad for children's health. This article looks at children's attitudes towards technology and sport.

One in four children class playing video games as "exercise", survey finds

23 per cent of young people surveyed viewed playing video games as a form of exercise raising fears that young people are becoming "hostages to handheld devices". 5

One in four British children believe that playing video games is a form of exercise according to a new report which warns that sport in schools is at a "critical crossroads".

10 Youth Sport Trust, a national charity which promotes physical education and sport, warned that young people risk becoming "hostages to handheld devices" after surveying 1,000 children aged between five and 16. 15

The survey found that while three quarters of children say they enjoy PE lessons and 40 per cent want to play more sport, 23 per cent of children thought that "playing a type of computer game with friends is a type of exercise." 20

The survey forms part of a study called "The Class of 2035", which warns that PE lessons in schools are crucial in order "to avoid a physically and socially disengaged future generation, over dependent on technology." 25

It is suggested that schools should look for ways to incorporate technology into sports lessons and explains that although "technology plays heavily in the lives of young people" this fondness for gadgets should not be taken "as a sign of young people's closed-mindedness to other forms of social activity." 30

35 The report concludes: "There is no resisting the march of technology. Policymakers can feel nostalgic for a time before the challenges new connected technologies have brought in engaging young people, or they can harness these technologies to their advantage." 40

"In order to get children active from a young age, a more holistic approach* to PE is needed, one which integrates technology and the delivery of a seamless, intuitive and digitally enhanced form of physical activity." 45

Ali Oliver, Chief Executive of the Youth Sport Trust who has worked in education and sports development for 20 years, said: "I think that we're starting to see changes in the way that primary schools are looking at and thinking about PE and sport, to see it much more as part of the holistic education of the child rather than a kind of bolt on, extra-curricular programme which I think, if the investment continues, probably in the next two to four years, we will see an increase in participation in primary schools as a result." 50 55

From *www.independent.co.uk/*

Glossary

a more holistic approach — a more rounded approach

1. **Do lines 1-5 present a positive or negative view of handheld devices? Explain your answer.**

....

.... 2 marks

2. **Find and copy an example of alliteration from lines 6-10.**
Why do you think the authors of the report chose this phrase?

....

....

.... 2 marks

3. **The majority of children questioned for the study (circle one):**

a. class video games as exercise b. enjoy PE lessons c. want to play more sport 1 mark

4. **Summarise lines 31-34 in your own words.**

....

.... 1 mark

5. **"the march of technology" in line 36 is an example of (circle one):**

a. personification b. a metaphor c. onomatopoeia d. a simile 1 mark

6. **In lines 41-45, which verb does the writer use that means "to include"?**

.... 1 mark

7. **Do you think Ali Oliver feels optimistic or pessimistic about the future of PE in primary schools? Explain your answer.**

.... 2 marks

....

....

Total out of 10

Cider With Rosie

Cider With Rosie **by Laurie Lee is an autobiographical novel, based on the author's own childhood. It is set in the rural village of Slad in Gloucestershire. This extract is set just before the end of World War One and describes the day Lee's family moved to Slad from the nearby town of Stroud.**

I was set down from the carrier's cart at the age of three; and there with a sense of bewilderment and terror my life in the village began.

The June grass, amongst which I stood, was taller than I was, and I wept. I had never been so close to grass before. It towered above me and all around me, each blade tattooed with tiger-skins of sunlight. It was knife-edged, dark, and a wicked green, thick as a forest and alive with grasshoppers that chirped and chattered and leapt through the air like monkeys.

I was lost and didn't know where to move. A tropic heat oozed up from the ground, rank with sharp odours of roots and nettles. Snow-clouds of elder-blossom banked in the sky, showering upon me the fumes and flakes of their sweet and giddy suffocation. High overhead ran frenzied larks, screaming, as though the sky were tearing apart.

For the first time in my life I was out of the sight of humans. For the first time in my life I was alone in a world whose behaviour I could neither predict nor fathom: a world of birds that squealed, of plants that stank, of insects that sprang about without warning. I was lost and I did not expect to be found again. I put back my head and howled, and the sun hit me smartly on the face, like a bully.

From this daylight nightmare I was awakened, as from many another, by the appearance of my sisters. They came scrambling and calling up the steep rough bank, and parting the long grass found me. Faces of rose, familiar, living; huge shining faces hung up like shields between me and the sky; faces with grins and white teeth (some broken) to be conjured up like genii with a howl, brushing off terror with their broad scoldings and affection. They leaned over me – one, two, three – their mouths smeared with red currants and their hands dripping with juice.

"There, there, it's all right, don't you wail any more. Come down 'ome and we'll stuff you with currants."

And Marjorie, the eldest, lifted me into her long brown hair, and ran me jogging down the path and through the steep rose-filled garden, and set me down on the cottage doorstep, which was our home, though I couldn't believe it.

An extract from *Cider With Rosie* by Laurie Lee.

1. **Give two reasons why the narrator is afraid when he is standing in the grass.**

....

.... 2 marks

2. **Write down one metaphor from lines 11-15 and explain its effect.**

....

....

.... 2 marks

3. **a. Which of the following techniques does the narrator use to describe the sun in line 20? Circle one.**

a. onomatopoeia   b. alliteration   c. a simile   d. repetition   1 mark

b. What effect does this description of the sun have on the reader?

....

.... 2 marks

4. **Why do you think the narrator compares his sisters' faces to "shields" (line 24)?**

....

.... 1 mark

5. **Do you find the narrator's description of the natural world in lines 4-20 surprising? Explain your answer.**

.... 2 marks

....

....

Total out of 10

Olympic Torch Relay, Day 52

In the seventy days before the start of the London 2012 Olympics, the Olympic torch made an 8,000 mile journey around the British Isles. 8,000 people were lucky enough to carry the torch for part of this journey. In this article, Matt King, one of the torchbearers, tells his story.

I'll be carrying the Olympic torch through Dunstable early on Monday morning, before eight o'clock, so hopefully the weather will have improved. I'm massively looking forward to it, of course.

I could never have foreseen how my life was going to pan out. Eight years ago I was
5 playing rugby league for the London Broncos colts side. We travelled to Halifax one weekend, stayed overnight, and on Sunday I was paralysed from the neck down, making a tackle. As I lay on the ground I knew straightaway what had happened to me and, for a boy of 17, it was devastating.

I was in Stoke Mandeville hospital for nine months (the torch will visit Stoke
10 Mandeville, birthplace of the Paralympic Games in 1948, shortly after I've done my leg of the relay) and found myself at a crossroads. I could either give up, or try to rebuild my life. So I went back to school and finished my A-levels, then went to the University of Hertfordshire, where I got a first-class degree in law. Now I work for a City law firm, where I have a training contract, working with clients with spinal and
15 brain injuries. They are quite complicated cases and I can have empathy with them.

This has been a surreal month for me. A few weeks ago a very official-looking letter dropped through my door box. It looked serious and I thought it may be about my tax. It was from the prime minister's office, telling me that I'd been given an OBE*. It came out of the blue and is a tremendous honour; when I told my mum, she cried. The
20 honour was, I suppose, for my charity work with people with spinal injuries. But I've not consciously looked for recognition. I've just tried in the last eight years since that fateful day to live as normal life as possible.

I know I won't be the last person to be paralysed in a sporting accident. It was a freak incident, and no one's fault – I don't hold any grudges. I knew rugby had its risks,
25 but you just think that accident is going to happen to someone else. I still follow rugby league and rugby union, though; in fact I got my RFU coaching badges after the accident and went back to my old union club in Biggleswade to coach the youngsters. They were great, but I found it tough as it emphasised what I couldn't do anymore.

Today will be great, though: a once-in-a-lifetime opportunity, and recognition for my
30 family, friends and all those strangers who have helped me after those dark times in 2004.

Glossary

OBE — Order of the British Empire, a special award for outstanding services to the community

1. **How did Matt rebuild his life after his accident?**

....

.... 1 mark

2. **Why is Matt able to have empathy with his clients?**

....

.... 1 mark

3. **Why do you think Matt describes the month as "surreal" (line 16)?**

....

.... 2 marks

4. **What does Matt mean by "that fateful day" in lines 21-22? Why do you think he describes it in this way?**

....

.... 2 marks

5. **How did Matt feel about coaching rugby? Why?**

....

.... 2 marks

6. **Matt says he felt devastated after his accident (line 8). Do you think he still feels this way? Explain your answer.**

.... 2 marks

....

....

Total out of 10

Poems about Seasons

Adrian Henri and John Updike were both born in 1932. Henri was a British poet and painter, while Updike was an American poet and writer. They are both known for writing poems that describe familiar scenes. In these poems, they use vivid language to bring the seasons to life.

Autumn

Season of conkers and fireworks
and mellow fruitfulness. New shoes,
and a coat that's a bit too big,
to grow into next year. Blackberries
5 along the canal, white jungles
of frost on the window. Leaves
to kick all the way home,
the smell of bonfires,
stamping the ice on puddles
10 into crazy paving. The nights come in
early, and you can't play out
after school. Soon
there'll be tangerines in the shops,
in shiny paper like Christmas lights.

15 The little ones write letters to Santa Claus.

The big ones laugh under the streetlights.

Adrian Henri

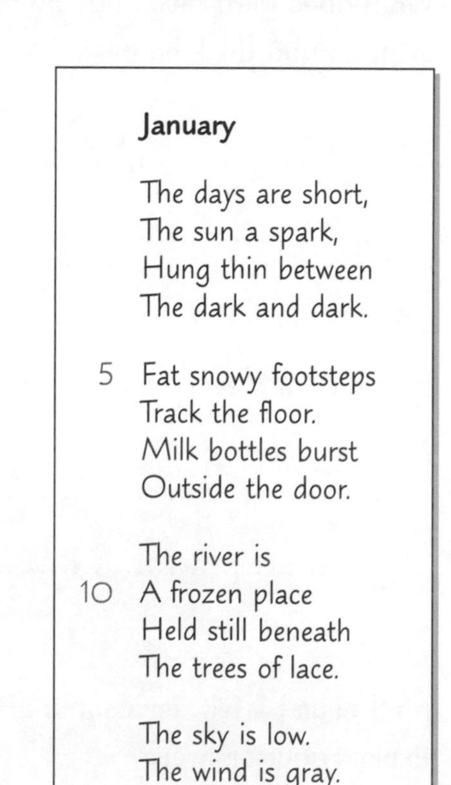

January

The days are short,
The sun a spark,
Hung thin between
The dark and dark.

5 Fat snowy footsteps
Track the floor.
Milk bottles burst
Outside the door.

The river is
10 A frozen place
Held still beneath
The trees of lace.

The sky is low.
The wind is gray.
15 The radiator
Purrs all day.

John Updike

1. In *January*, the poet says in line 1 that the "days are short". Which phrase from *Autumn* describes short days?

....

1 mark

2. Find and copy a simile from lines 1-14 of *Autumn*.

....

1 mark

3. What does the poet mean by "trees of lace" in line 12 of *January*?

....

....

1 mark

4. Why do you think the poet chose the verb "purrs" to describe the sound of the radiator in line 16 of *January*?

....

....

2 marks

5. Which poem is written in free verse?

....

1 mark

6. Which poem do you think is more positive about the season it describes? Explain your answer.

....

....

2 marks

7. Which poem do you prefer? Explain your answer.

....

....

....

2 marks

Total out of 10

A Letter from C.S. Lewis

C.S. Lewis was a British author and academic. He wrote many books for children and adults. His best-known children's books are *The Chronicles of Narnia*, a series of seven fantasy novels. In this abridged version of his letter, Lewis offers one of his fans advice on how to write well.

26 June 1956

Dear Joan–

Thanks for your letter of the 3rd. You describe your Wonderful Night v. well. That is, you describe the place and the people and the night and the feeling of it all, very well — but not the *thing* itself — the setting but not the jewel. And no wonder! Wordsworth often does just the same. His *Prelude* (you're bound to read it about 10 years hence. Don't try it now, or you'll only spoil it for later reading) is full of moments in which everything except the *thing* itself is described. If you become a writer you'll be trying to describe the *thing* all your life: and lucky if, out of dozens of books, one or two sentences, just for a moment, come near to getting it across.

[...]

What really matters is:–

1. Always try to use the language so as to make quite clear what you mean and make sure your sentence couldn't mean anything else.

2. Always prefer the plain direct word to the long, vague one. Don't *implement* promises, but *keep* them.

3. Never use abstract nouns when concrete ones will do. If you mean "More people died" don't say "Mortality rose."

4. In writing. Don't use adjectives which merely tell us how you want us to *feel* about the thing you are describing. I mean, instead of telling us a thing was "terrible," describe it so that we'll be terrified. Don't say it was "delightful"; make *us* say "delightful" when we've read the description. You see, all those words (horrifying, wonderful, hideous, exquisite) are only like saying to your readers, "Please will you do my job for me."

5. Don't use words too big for the subject. Don't say "infinitely" when you mean "very"; otherwise you'll have no word left when you want to talk about something *really* infinite.

Thanks for the photos. You and Aslan both look v. well. I hope you'll like your new home.

With love,
yours

C.S. Lewis

1. **What metaphor does Lewis use to comment on the way Joan described her "Wonderful Night"?**

....

1 mark

2. **In your own words, explain why Lewis tells Joan not to read Wordsworth's *Prelude* until she is older.**

....

....

2 marks

3. **Do you think Lewis finds describing "the *thing* itself" easy or difficult? Explain your answer.**

....

....

2 marks

4. **In lines 12-13, Lewis advises Joan to avoid (circle one):**

a. repetition **b.** contradictions **c.** exaggeration **d.** ambiguity

1 mark

5. **What does this letter tell you about how you should use adjectives in your writing?**

....

....

2 marks

6. **In your own words, summarise the advice that Lewis offers about writing in lines 12-26.**

....

....

....

2 marks

Total out of 10

The Lord of the Rings

The Lord of the Rings **by J.R.R. Tolkien is one of the most popular novels ever written. Approximately 150 million copies have been sold since it was published in the 1950s. In this extract, Gandalf (a wizard) is travelling to the city of Minas Tirith with Pippin (a hobbit).**

Pippin looked out from the shelter of Gandalf's cloak. He wondered if he was awake or still sleeping, still in the swift-moving dream in which he had been wrapped so long since the great ride began. The dark world was rushing by and the wind sang loudly in his ears. He could see nothing but the wheeling stars, and away to his right vast shadows
5 against the sky where the mountains of the South marched past. Sleepily he tried to reckon the times and stages of their journey, but his memory was drowsy and uncertain.

There had been the first ride at terrible speed without a halt, and then in the dawn he had seen a pale gleam of gold, and they had come to the silent town and the great empty house on the hill. And hardly had they reached its shelter when the winged shadow
10 had passed over once again, and men wilted with fear. But Gandalf had spoken soft words to him, and he had slept in a corner, tired but uneasy, dimly aware of comings and goings and of men talking and Gandalf giving orders. And then again riding, riding in the night. This was the second, no, the third night since he had looked in the Stone. And with that hideous memory he woke fully, and shivered, and the noise of the wind became filled with
15 menacing voices.

A light kindled in the sky, a blaze of yellow fire behind dark barriers. Pippin cowered back, afraid for a moment, wondering into what dreadful country Gandalf was bearing him. He rubbed his eyes, and then he saw that it was the moon rising above the eastern shadows, now almost at the full. So the night was not yet old and for hours the
20 dark journey would go on. He stirred and spoke.

'Where are we, Gandalf?' he asked.

'In the realm of Gondor,' the wizard answered. 'The land of Anórien is still passing by.'

There was a silence again for a while. Then, 'What is that?' cried Pippin suddenly, clutching at Gandalf's cloak. 'Look! Fire, red fire! Are there dragons in this land? Look,
25 there is another!'

An extract from *The Lord of the Rings: The Return of the King* by J.R.R. Tolkien.

1. Find and copy an example of personification from the first paragraph.

....

1 mark

2. In the first paragraph, how does Tolkien show that Gandalf and Pippin are moving quickly?

....

....

....

2 marks

3. What does the phrase "men wilted with fear" in line 10 mean?

....

....

1 mark

4. Why do you think Tolkien repeats the word "riding" in line 12?

....

....

1 mark

5. What do you think the word "menacing" (line 15) means? Check your answer in a dictionary.

....

1 mark

6. How do you think Pippin feels in the last paragraph of the extract? Explain your answer.

....

....

2 marks

7. Do you think Pippin trusts Gandalf? Explain your answer.

....

....

....

2 marks

Total out of 10

Queen Victoria's Diary

Early in the morning on the 20th June 1837, King William IV of Great Britain died. He was succeeded by his niece, Victoria, who was just 18 years old. Queen Victoria went on to reign for 63 years. In this extract from her diary, Victoria describes the morning she became Queen.

Tuesday, 20 June 1837

I was awoke at 6 o'clock by Mamma, who told me that the Archbishop of Canterbury and Lord Conyngham were here, and wished to see me. I got out of bed and went into my sitting-room (only in my dressing-gown), and alone, and saw them. Lord Conyngham (the Lord Chamberlain) then acquainted me that my poor Uncle, the King, was no more, and had expired at 12 minutes p.2 this morning, and consequently that I am Queen. Lord Conyngham knelt down and kissed my hand, at the same time delivering to me the official announcement of the poor King's demise. The Archbishop then told me that the Queen was desirous that he should come and tell me the details of the last moments of my poor, good Uncle; he said that he had directed his mind to religion, and had died in a perfectly happy, quiet state of mind, and was quite prepared for his death. He added that the King's sufferings at the last were not very great but that there was a good deal of uneasiness. Lord Conyngham, whom I charged to express my feelings of condolence and sorrow to the poor Queen, returned directly to Windsor. I then went to my room and dressed. Since it has pleased Providence to place me in this station, I shall do my utmost to fulfil my duty towards my country; I am very young and perhaps in many, though not in all things, inexperienced, but I am sure, that very few have more real good will and more real desire to do what is fit and right than I have.

***

At 9 came Lord Melbourne, whom I saw in my room, and of course quite alone as I shall always do all my Ministers. He kissed my hand and I then acquainted him that it had long been my intention to retain him and the rest of the present Ministry at the head of affairs, and that it could not be in better hands than his. … He then read to me the Declaration which I was to read to the Council, which he wrote himself and which is a very fine one. I then talked with him some little time longer after which he left me. … I like him very much and feel confidence in him. He is a very straightforward, honest, clever and good man. I then wrote a letter to the Queen.

An extract from Queen Victoria's diary.

1. **What does the word "expired" (line 6) mean? Check your answer in a dictionary.**

....

1 mark

2. **Which verb could be used instead of "acquainted" in lines 5 and 20?**

....

1 mark

3. **Why did the Archbishop of Canterbury come to see Victoria?**

....

....

1 mark

4. **What does Victoria mean by "this station" (line 15)?**

....

1 mark

5. **What qualities does Victoria have that she thinks will make her a good queen?**

....

....

2 marks

6. **What is Victoria's opinion of Lord Melbourne? Explain your answer with evidence from the text.**

....

....

2 marks

7. **How do you think Victoria felt when she heard that she was Queen? Explain your answer.**

....

2 marks

....

....

Total
out of 10

If—

Rudyard Kipling wrote lots of books and poems for children, including *The Jungle Book* and the *Just So Stories*. He wrote *If—* for his son, John. Although this poem was written more than 100 years ago, it is still very popular, and has even been voted the nation's favourite poem.

If you can keep your head when all about you
  Are losing theirs and blaming it on you,
If you can trust yourself when all men doubt you,
  But make allowance for their doubting too;
5 If you can wait and not be tired by waiting,
  Or being lied about, don't deal in lies,
Or being hated, don't give way to hating,
  And yet don't look too good, nor talk too wise:

If you can dream—and not make dreams your master;
10 If you can think—and not make thoughts your aim;
If you can meet with Triumph and Disaster
  And treat those two impostors just the same;
If you can bear to hear the truth you've spoken
  Twisted by knaves to make a trap for fools,
15 Or watch the things you gave your life to, broken,
  And stoop and build 'em up with worn-out tools:

If you can make one heap of all your winnings
  And risk it on one turn of pitch-and-toss,
And lose, and start again at your beginnings
20 And never breathe a word about your loss;
If you can force your heart and nerve and sinew
  To serve your turn long after they are gone,
And so hold on when there is nothing in you
  Except the Will which says to them: 'Hold on!'

25 If you can talk with crowds and keep your virtue,
  Or walk with Kings—nor lose the common touch,
If neither foes nor loving friends can hurt you,
  If all men count with you, but none too much;
If you can fill the unforgiving minute
30 With sixty seconds' worth of distance run,
Yours is the Earth and everything that's in it,
  And—which is more—you'll be a Man, my son!

Rudyard Kipling

1. Is this poem written in the first, second or third person?

....

1 mark

2. Look at lines 1-8. Copy out the line which tells the reader to be patient.

....

1 mark

3. According to the poem, if people tell lies about you, you should (circle one):

a. tell lies   b. stay calm   c. trust yourself   d. not tell lies

1 mark

4. "If you can force your heart and nerve and sinew / To serve your turn long after they are gone" (lines 21-22). Which word best sums up these lines?

a. arrogance   b. perseverance   c. self-confidence   d. complacency

1 mark

5. What do you think the word "virtue" (line 25) means? Check your answer in a dictionary.

....

1 mark

6. "the unforgiving minute" in line 29 is an example of (circle one):

a. a simile   b. a metaphor   c. personification   d. onomatopoeia

1 mark

7. Do you think it would be easy or difficult to treat "Triumph and Disaster" "just the same" (lines 11-12)? Explain your answer.

....

....

2 marks

8. Do you think *If—* gives good advice about how people should behave? Explain your answer.

....

2 marks

....

....

Total out of 10

Theseus's Adventures

Theseus was a great hero in Greek mythology. As a young man, he set out on the difficult and dangerous journey from his birthplace, Troezen, to the Greek capital, Athens. He experienced many adventures during his journey. This extract describes two of those adventures.

Theseus continued his journey in peace, until he came to the Isthmus of Corinth, where two adventures awaited him. The first was with a cruel giant named Sinis, nicknamed The Pine-bender, whose usual practice was to bend some huge pine until its top touched the ground, and call to any unsuspecting passer-by to seize it and 5 lend him a helping hand for a moment. Then, as soon as the innocent stranger had complied with his request, he would suddenly let go the pine, which, freed from his gigantic grasp, sprang back to its upright position, and hurled the unfortunate traveler way up in the air, to be dashed to pieces against the rocky mountain side.

Theseus, who had already heard of the giant's 10 stratagem*, skillfully eluded the danger, and finally caused Sinis to perish by the same cruel death which he had dealt out to so many others.

In one place the Isthmus of Corinth was exceedingly narrow, and the only practicable pathway led 15 along a rocky ledge, guarded by a robber named Sciron, who forced all who tried to pass him to wash his feet. While the traveler was thus engaged, and knelt in the narrow pathway to do his bidding, he would suddenly raise his foot, kick him over the side, and hurl him down into the sea below, where a huge tortoise was ever waiting with gaping jaws 20 to devour the victims.

Instead of yielding* to Sciron's exactions*, Theseus drew his sword, and by his determined bearing so terrified the robber, that he offered him a free passage. This offer, however, did not satisfy Theseus, who said he would sheathe his sword only on condition that Sciron performed for him the menial office* he had imposed upon so 25 many others. Sciron dared not refuse, and obeyed in fear and trembling; but he was doomed never to molest* any one again, for Theseus kicked him over the precipice*, into the breakers, where the tortoise feasted upon his remains with as keen a relish as upon former victims.

An abridged extract from *Myths of Greece and Rome* by H.A. Guerber.

Glossary

stratagem — trick	exactions — demands	molest — attack
yielding — giving in	menial office — lowly task	precipice — steep cliff

1 **What do you think the word "eluded" (line 10) means? Check your answer in a dictionary.**

....

1 mark

2 **How did Theseus conquer Sinis?**

....

....

1 mark

3 **Why were people travelling on the Isthmus of Corinth unable to avoid Sciron?**

....

....

2 marks

4 **In the third paragraph, which verb does the writer use that means "to eat"?**

....

1 mark

5 **How did Sciron feel when he was forced to wash Theseus's feet?**
Why do you think he felt this way?

....

....

2 marks

6 **Identify one feature of the text that suggests it is a myth.**

....

1 mark

7 **Do you think Theseus survived the journey to Athens? Explain your answer.**

....

....

....

2 marks

Total
out of 10

I Can Jump Puddles

Alan Marshall was born in a small town in southeastern Australia in 1902. As a child, he suffered from Infantile Paralysis, also known as polio. This illness left Alan unable to walk without crutches. In this extract, Alan describes how the people around him reacted when he fell ill.

I had not long started school when I contracted Infantile Paralysis. The epidemic that began in Victoria in the early 1900s moved into the country districts from the more populated areas, striking down children on isolated farms and in bush homes. I was the only victim in Turalla, and the people for miles around heard of my illness with a feeling of dread. They associated the word 'Paralysis' with idiocy, and the query 'Have you heard if his mind is affected?' was asked from many a halted buggy*, the driver leaning over the wheel for a yarn* with a friend met on the road.

For a few weeks the neighbours drove quickly past our house, looking hurriedly, with a new interest, at the old picket fence, the unbroken colts* in the stockyard and my tricycle lying on its side by the chaff house*. They called their children in earlier, wrapped them more warmly and gazed at them anxiously when they coughed or sneezed.

'It hits you like a blow from God,' said Mr Carter, the baker, who believed that this was so. He was the Superintendent of the Bible Class and proclaimed in his weekly announcements, as he faced his pupils with a sombre look:

'Next Sunday morning at Divine Service the Rev. Walter Robertson, B.A., will offer up prayers for the speedy recovery of this brave boy sorely stricken with a fell* disease. A full attendance is requested.'

Father, after hearing of these words, stood in the street one day tugging at his sandy moustache with a nervous, troubled hand, while he explained to Mr Carter just how I happened to catch the disease.

'They say you breathe the germ in,' he said. 'It's just floating about in the air – everywhere. You never know where it is. It must have been just floating past his nose when he breathed in and that was the end of him. He went down like a pole-axed* steer*. If he'd been breathing out when that germ passed he'd've been right.'

He paused, then added sadly, 'Now you're praying for him.'

An extract from *I Can Jump Puddles* by Alan Marshall.

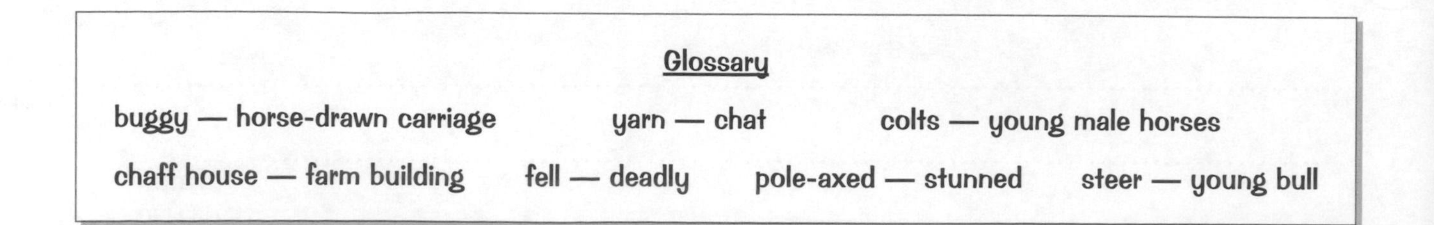

Glossary

buggy — horse-drawn carriage
yarn — chat
colts — young male horses
chaff house — farm building
fell — deadly
pole-axed — stunned
steer — young bull

1 **Which word could the author have used in line 5 instead of "query"?**

....

1 mark

2 **a. Which of the following words best describes the local community's response to Alan's illness? Circle one.**

a. happiness   b. anger   c. confusion   d. curiosity

1 mark

b. Use evidence from the text to explain your answer to part a.

....

....

2 marks

3 **Why do you think people wrapped their children up "more warmly" (line 11) while Alan was ill?**

....

....

1 mark

4 **Write down one simile from lines 8-14.**

....

1 mark

5 **Do you think Alan's father felt optimistic or pessimistic about Alan's chances of recovery? Explain your answer.**

....

....

2 marks

6 **The title of Alan's book is *I Can Jump Puddles*. What does this title suggest about Alan's attitude towards his disability? Explain your answer.**

....

2 marks

....

....

Total out of 10

White Fang

White Fang **is a novel by the American author, Jack London. It is set in the Yukon Territory in north-western Canada, and tells the story of a wild wolfdog called White Fang. In this extract, White Fang is getting ready to escape from his first master, a native American called Grey Beaver.**

In the fall of the year, when the days were shortening and the bite of the frost was coming into the air, White Fang got his chance for liberty. For several days there had been a great hubbub in the village. The summer camp was being dismantled, and the tribe, bag and baggage, was preparing to go off to the fall hunting. White Fang watched it all with eager (5) eyes, and when the tepees began to come down and the canoes were loading at the bank, he understood. Already the canoes were departing, and some had disappeared down the river.

Quite deliberately he determined to stay behind. He waited his opportunity to slink out of camp to the woods. Here, in the (10) running stream where ice was beginning to form, he hid his trail. Then he crawled into the heart of a dense thicket and waited. The time passed by, and he slept intermittently for hours. Then he was aroused by Grey Beaver's voice calling (15) him by name. There were other voices. White Fang could hear Grey Beaver's squaw taking part in the search, and Mit-sah, who was Grey Beaver's son.

White Fang trembled with fear, and though the impulse came to crawl out of his hiding-place, he resisted it. After a time the voices died away, and some time after that he crept out to enjoy the success of his undertaking. Darkness was coming on, and for a while (20) he played about among the trees, pleasuring in his freedom. Then, and quite suddenly, he became aware of loneliness. He sat down to consider, listening to the silence of the forest and perturbed by it. That nothing moved nor sounded, seemed ominous. He felt the lurking of danger, unseen and unguessed. He was suspicious of the looming bulks of the trees and of the dark shadows that might conceal all manner of perilous things.

(25) Then it was cold. Here was no warm side of a tepee against which to snuggle. The frost was in his feet, and he kept lifting first one fore-foot and then the other. He curved his bushy tail around to cover them, and at the same time he saw a vision. There was nothing strange about it. Upon his inward sight was impressed a succession of memory-pictures. He saw the camp again, the tepees, and the blaze of the fires. He heard the shrill voices of (30) the women, the gruff basses of the men, and the snarling of the dogs. He was hungry, and he remembered pieces of meat and fish that had been thrown him. Here was no meat, nothing but a threatening and inedible silence.

An extract from *White Fang* by Jack London.

1. In line 6, Jack London says White Fang "understood". What do you think he understood?

....

.... 2 marks

2. How does White Fang feel when Grey Beaver is looking for him? Why do you think this is?

....

.... 1 mark

3. What do you think the word "ominous" (line 22) means? Check your answer in a dictionary.

.... 1 mark

4. How do you think White Fang feels in lines 20-24? How does Jack London show this?

....

....

.... 2 marks

5. What effect does the phrase "the frost was in his feet" (lines 25-26) have on the reader?

....

.... 2 marks

6. Why do you think White Fang didn't return to the camp when he was cold and hungry?

.... 2 marks

....

....

Total out of 10

Macbeth

William Shakespeare lived more than 400 years ago. Many people see him as the greatest writer in the English language. *Macbeth* is one of Shakespeare's best-known plays. In this scene, Macbeth and his friend Banquo are travelling to the town of Forres when they meet three witches.

Enter MACBETH *and* BANQUO.

MACBETH: So foul and fair a day I have not seen.

BANQUO: How far is't called to Forres? What are these,
So withered and so wild in their attire*,
That look not like th'inhabitants o'th'earth, 5
And yet are on't? Live you, or are you aught*
That man may question? You seem to understand me,
By each at once her choppy finger laying
Upon her skinny lips; you should be women,
And yet your beards forbid me to interpret 10
That you are so.

MACBETH: Speak if you can: what are you?

FIRST WITCH: All hail Macbeth! Hail to thee, Thane* of Glamis!

SECOND WITCH: All hail Macbeth! Hail to thee, Thane of Cawdor!

THIRD WITCH: All hail Macbeth that shalt be king hereafter! 15

BANQUO: Good sir, why do you start, and seem to fear
Things that do sound so fair? I'th'name of truth
Are ye fantastical*, or that indeed
Which outwardly ye show? My noble partner
You greet with present grace and great prediction 20
Of noble having and of royal hope,
That he seems rapt withal*. To me you speak not.
If you can look into the seeds of time
And say which grain will grow and which will not,
Speak then to me, who neither beg nor fear 25
Your favours nor your hate.

FIRST WITCH: Hail!

SECOND WITCH: Hail!

THIRD WITCH: Hail!

An extract from Act I, Scene 3 of *Macbeth* by William Shakespeare.

Glossary

attire — clothes
Thane — a person holding some of the King's land
rapt withal — amazed
aught — anything
fantastical — imaginary

1. "not like th'inhabitants o'th'earth" (line 5). Three letters are missing from this phrase. Rewrite it below, replacing the apostrophes with the appropriate letters.

   ....

   2 marks

2. In your own words, describe what The Witches look like.

   ....

   ....

   2 marks

3. Why is Banquo uncertain whether The Witches are men or women?

   ....

   ....

   1 mark

4. What does line 16 tell you about Macbeth's reaction to The Witches' prophecy that he will become king?

   ....

   ....

   1 mark

5. Find and copy a phrase from lines 16-21 which shows that Banquo isn't sure whether The Witches are real or not.

   ....

   1 mark

6. "look into the seeds of time / And say which grain will grow" (lines 23-24). This is an example of (circle one):

   a. onomatopoeia b. personification c. a metaphor d. a simile

   1 mark

7. Do you think Banquo is afraid of The Witches? Explain your answer.

   ....

   2 marks

   ....

   ....

Total out of 10

Change Your Journey to School

By now, you've had plenty of practice at reading texts and answering questions. Now it's time to write your own text, think of some questions, and then swap with a friend.

Write a text that will persuade young people to walk or cycle to school rather than going by car. You could include health and environmental benefits, and you should use really persuasive language.

E6CW21